SCARY FAIRY'S TALES

STORIES AND POEMS WITH A WICKED TWIST

Dear Patti —

Enjoy my "Wicked
Twist" on fairy tales!

Love,

Donna Puglisi

SCARY FAIRY'S TALES

STORIES AND POEMS WITH A WICKED TWIST

DONNA PUGLISI

MOUNTAIN ARBOR PRESS

MOUNTAIN ARBOR
PRESS
Alpharetta, GA

ISBN: 978-1-6653-0424-5 - Paperback
eISBN: 978-1-6653-0425-2 - ePub

Printed in the United States of America   0 5 1 3 2 2

∞ This paper meets the requirements of ANSI/NISO Z39.48-1992 (Permanence of Paper)

WARNING!

This book is not for the faint of heart! You think the Grimm Brothers were bad? Scary Fairy has them beat.

If you want to give your children nightmares, screaming in their little beds, this book is for you.

These stories and poems will scare the crap out of anyone.

SCARY FAIRY

OTHER POETRY BOOKS BY DONNA PUGLISI

"CHRISTMAS POEMS BY THE FIREPLACE"

"I'M NO ANGEL IN STILETTOS, THERE'S A LITTLE DEVIL IN ALL OF US"

"THE POWER OF PASSION, DANCING BAREFOOT"

"ROSES AND ONIONS, ONE LAYER AT A TIME"

"DIAMONDS IN THE ROUGH"

SCARY FAIRY'S TALES

Beware of the Scary Fairy!
She spins such wicked tales.
Crooked teeth, a bony nose,
Skin like a lizard's scales.

This is how Scary Fairy came to be,
Turn these pages carefully!
Don't read the dreadful tales at night,
Children quiver and shake with fright.

She'll creep into sweet little dreams,
Oh, how she loves to hear their screams!

THE BEGINNING

HOW THE SCARY FAIRY CAME TO BE

Scary Mary wasn't always a fairy. She was just a very scary person. One day she arrived in Fairyville and asked the Queen Fairy if she could join them and become a fairy. Well, the Queen Fairy asked for some credentials. Scary Mary didn't have any.

The Queen Fairy took Scary Mary in anyway. She tried to teach her the ways of being a good fairy, doing great magical things, especially with children.

Scary Mary didn't like children. In fact, she hated the little buggers. But, she thought she could get over that, and agreed to go into training at the Fairy Academy. She was sprinkled with fairy dust and sprouted wings. She could fly anywhere! Scary Mary liked that part. That meant she could take off and go wherever and whenever she pleased. So she thought.

After a while, Scary Mary acquired many talents. But she also hated the good fairies because they were so boring and felt they were all "goodie two shoes". She wanted more. She wanted to scare the diapers off of kids, giving them nightmares and screaming with horror!

The Queen Fairy got wind of her schemes and finally kicked Scary Mary out of Fairyville. The Sugar Plum Fairy banned her from her plum vineyards because she withered them on the vines! The Tooth Fairy exiled her to the Nether World of Bad Fairies. This happened after Scary Mary stole teeth from children and replaced them with slithering worms that wiggled under their pillows. So, Scary Mary became "Scary Fairy" and went out on her own. If you dare to read these Scary Fairy's Tales to your children, you won't sleep well either.

CONTENTS

"SCARY FAIRY'S TALES"

THE CHILDREN'S TREE

Once upon a time, there was a beautiful tree that
shimmered in the sun. It was in the middle of a forest far
from everyone.
Local villagers began to talk,
"Don't dare enter, don't go for a walk!
Our children are missing, where did they go?
A demon took them far below!"
Why did the children disappear?
They were lured to the forest, we fear.
A shimmering tree sang its bewitching song,
Like the Piper, they danced along.
Skipping and laughing, one by one,
The shimmering tree grabbed the young.
Wrapped in leaves from head to toe,
No child was spared,
Into the tree did go.
Becoming part of tree's old wood,
Little faces of bark then stood.
Glisten and shine, hear them whine!
Their screams were never heard.
Not even a whisper, not even a sigh,
Not a single song from a bird.

Protect your children, cover their ears,
Don't walk in the Forest of Fears!
Each budding flower, every new leaf
are parents tears and heartbroken grief.

MARY HAD LAMB CHOPS

"Mary had a little lamb, little lamb, little lamb..Baa Baa Baa!" Or should we say, "Blah, Blah, Blah!" Any way you sing that silly song, what really went wrong?

Mary loved lamb. She loved lamb chops, lamb burgers, lamb meatballs. No matter how you cooked those cute little things, she ate it. In fact, Mary loved lamb so much, she even took one to school and had the children pet and massage it all day so that it would be tender and juicy. How sick was that? She could have had Kobe cows and massage the crap out of those.

But let's get back to Mary and her lambs. She was so obsessed with them that she drove a "Lambergini", her version of the Italian sports car. Eventually, Mary ran out of little lambs. The town folk accused her of lamb harvesting and stealing from their farms. She felt very "sheepish" and tried to "pull the wool over their eyes" by becoming a vegetarian. They didn't buy it and ran Mary out of town.

We still think she has a sheep ranch somewhere in Argentina.

Baa! Baa! Baa!

SHADOW MAN

Lurking around the corner is the Shadow Man, creeping along walls, hiding under stairs. He slithers silently, trying to snatch your shadow to put it in his "Shadow Box". Now, who would want to live without a shadow? It would mean you didn't exist at all!

Shadow Man, Shadow Man,
Run, dear children, as fast as you can!
Hide your shadows under the covers,
Don't open your eyes! On the ceiling he hovers.

He stores your shadow in his "Shadow Box",
Seals it with his magic locks.
If you see the Shadow Man hiding behind your door,
Grab him, stab him with a stick,
Lock him in a drawer.

Bury him deep within the ground,
Do it quietly, don't make a sound!
He'll try to get into your head with nightmares filling you
with dread.

Wear your shadow, stitch it tight
with magic threads when you sleep at night.
Don't let it escape like Peter Pan,
It's death for Mr. Shadow Man!

PUMPKIN PIE

"Trick or treat! Trick or treat! Give us something good to eat!"
Little goblins at your door,
With open bags, they beg for more.
How to lure them to the field where Jack O'Lantern feeds?
Far away from well-lit streets
to his home of swamps and weeds.

Old Jack is hungry, craving pies,
Filled with children's tiny eyes.
He eats sweet meat right off their bones,
With a wicked smile he wails and moans.

"I'm going to make my pumpkin pies
under the moon and starry skies.
It's Halloween and I will eat
each little child for "Trick or Treat"!

Gathering 'round, they heard the sound
of Jack O'Lantern's song.
To the fields through woods and streams
The children danced along.

Faster, faster, twirling to the loud hypnotic beat,
Down they fell, one by one,
No child was on his feet.

Covered with magic pumpkin seeds,
He dissolved their bones, on them he feeds.
When his pumpkin pies were done,
He gazed upon the rising sun.
"Now I have my pumpkin pies to last another year!"
Next Halloween beware of Jack,
He'll need more pies, we fear.

Cover your children's tiny ears,
Don't listen to his tune!
That smiling face is wicked Jack
when you gaze upon the moon!

THE FOUNTAIN
OF YOUTHS

"Once upon a time.." Shall we start with that tired old fairy tale line? Scary Fairy wants to spin you a tale of the witch's fountain. It was so enticing, so beautiful to behold! Watery fingers dangled and splashed into the fountain's bowl. It was the "The Fountain of Youths". But don't be fooled. Sometimes things aren't always as they seem!

There was a garden path with pretty flowers blooming alongside it. Every color in the world sparkled through large evergreens, weeping willows, and huge oak trees. You see, in this valley there was every kind of tree and flower you could imagine. In the middle of this lush green valley was a beautiful fountain. It glistened in the sun and its rivulets of flowing water looked like long fingers dancing and splashing into the fountain's huge bowl.

Not far away lived an old woman. Her house was made of twigs and leaves. It was held together by strong roots from trees which bound the house together. The roof was thatched tightly, so that it could never blow away in a storm. The old woman cast a mighty spell on her house to make it invisible if she wanted to hide from nosy villagers. Most of the town folk avoided her anyway. They were scared to death!

You see, she was a very, very powerful witch. This particular witch was many centuries old. The secret to her

6

long life was simple. She fed on children. Not like the witch in Hansel and Gretel. She drank children's tears and fed on their fears. The sparkling fountain's salty waters were all the tears from these children.

The more tears the witch drank from her fountain, the younger she became. When the fountain ran dry, she searched for more children. What became of them after she drained their tears? They were turned into flowers and trees, even the gnarly roots that bound her house together. Nobody would ever suspect their child was one of these!

The wicked witch transformed herself into a beautiful young woman when she went into the village. There were always more children to steal. There were more tears to fill her "Fountain of Youths". Also, there were more trees and flowers to plant.

If you see a beautiful fountain in the village square, just remember..BEWARE! Don't dare drink from the fountain because

THE OLD WITCH IS WATCHING!

FINGERNAILS ON THE CHALKBOARD

"Scratch, scratch, scratch"

The hair on the back of my neck stood up. Fingernails on the chalkboard! We all cringed at the annoying sound. It continued for ten minutes. The scary thing is, there was nobody at the chalkboard! It sounded as if the noise came from inside the board. How can that be?

Long nails scraped the chalkboard slowly and deliberately. Something was trying to get our attention or get out. I was only ten years old at the time. I will never forget that day in the classroom. All the kids were mesmerized and stared at the board as the scratching continued. Our teacher didn't know what to do. She was horrified!

All of a sudden there appeared a message that read "Help me!" We all rushed to the board and started screaming, "Who are you? What's wrong?"

The teacher's eyes were as big as saucers. Her mouth was wide open but she didn't say a word. Little did we know the board was cursed. A long time ago, it was in the possession of a dark voodoo queen. She used it as a huge Ouija board to summon demons in her black magic rituals. How it ended up in our classroom was a mystery, indeed.

The board began to bleed. It bled and bled and bled some more. Then we heard a horrible scream. "She's killing me! Help!"

The screech was deafening. Children were running out of the room. Teacher fainted on the spot.

"Voodoo Queen cursed my soul and locked me in this wretched board! I'm part of the Ouija, left to die. A prisoner of the board am I!"

I picked up the erasers and started to bang them together. Chalk was flying everywhere. It was on the board, in my hair, my face. It soaked up the blood flowing from the board.

"Thank you, dear child. I am finally free! The chalk has released me!"

Long black fingernails clawed their way out of the board, reaching out with veined bloody hands. I was frozen with fear. Then I saw her ugly twisted face. She crawled out of the board. Black spiders were in her hair. She gave me a wicked stare.

"Fooled you, stupid child! I am the Voodoo Witch who was banished into the board until you released me. Thank you from the bottom of my rotten black heart!"

With that, the evil board disintegrated into dust. A black ominous cloud appeared and floated out an open window, bringing torrential rain and thunder. I realized I was to blame for setting the Voodoo Witch free to wreak havoc on the world.

She still haunts my dreams. Late at night I can still hear "Scratch, scratch, scratch" on the chalkboard!

CARNIVORE CARNIVAL

Cotton candy spun with spider webs. Salted maggots in peanut shells. Beware, little ones! Hold tight to your parent's hand. You might be snatched and stretched like a tight rubber band. You could be turned into a wooden horse on the merry-go-round with no way to cry for help, no way to make a sound. Welcome to the CARNIVORE CARNIVAL!

"Step up, one and all! See the two-headed lady, the incredible shrinking man, our dog-faced boy with a tail! If you dare enter through these doors, you will find our insatiable carnivores are waiting to taste every single one of you, especially the children! So sweet and tangy, so delectable to munch on. Carnivore Clowns love to eat the little ones. Are you sure you want a ticket?"

One by one, the amused crowd passed through the turnstile, anticipating an exciting show. They wanted to be thrilled and scared to death. Little did they know that's exactly what would happen.

The lights dimmed as the Carnivore Clowns danced in and out of the aisles. Popcorn littered the floor as bags squirmed with something vile and white inside. Screaming children and parents turned pale, tossing the writhing insects onto the floor. Flesh eaters!

Attaching themselves to the legs of bystanders, these bloodsuckers ate through skin and bone so quickly there was no time to run. Panic and chaos ensued. Multiplying by the hundreds, they flew through the air like mosquitoes. The white flesh eaters slithered into hair, eyes, and ears. Then came the Carnivore Clowns!

Their white makeup was smeared with blood. Laughing with wicked delight, each bite of juicy flesh made them thirst for more. Carnivore Carnival was now in full swing.

People ran in all directions, clawing at the doors which were bolted shut. Children screamed, clinging to their parents, who fell to the ground as the vampire feast continued.

There was dead silence after two hours of carnage. Not one person was alive. Bits and pieces of bodies not consumed were quickly put in huge containers. The blood was mopped up. There was no evidence of any slaughter at all!

Ah, the smell of popcorn! So enticing, it wafted through the air. The circus crowd gathered around the Ring Master's stage outside the tent.

"Step up, one and all!"

THE VORACIOUS BODACIOUS MERMAID

On the rocky shores of an island far, far away, you can see many shipwrecks. They are haunting reminders of the tragic deaths of sailors who succumbed to the mermaid's siren song. She was the Voracious Bodacious Mermaid!

Shimmering scales on her tail glistened in the sun as the beautiful mermaid splashed in the ocean's warm water. She was a sailor's demise if he looked in her deep blue eyes.

Lured by her bewitching songs, many a ship had struck the dangerous rocks and sank with all the crew drowning and screaming in terror. Another jeweled scale to add to the mermaid's tail!

On a blustery stormy night, the ocean raged on with waves reaching forty feet high. The sky turned black, as thunder roared, spitting out bolts of lightning, occasionally lighting up the sky to reveal the outline of a ship. Tossed like a toy, the ship rocked and rolled at the mercy of the ocean's wrath.

Sailors clung to the rails for dear life. The Captain, a swarthy man with a long gray beard, held tight to the wheel. It seemed as if all was lost and they would sink to the bottom of Davey Jones' locker.

Then, as if by a miracle, they heard her song. Piercing the cold cruel winds, her voice was like a choir of angels. It sounded as if the sky exploded in a heavenly chorus. The crew was hypnotized. Captain Smyth stood motionless, hands tightly gripping the ship's wheel.

Rising out of the water, the mermaid's enticing dance in and out of the waves was a spectacle to behold! Her shimmering scales seemed to glow in the dark. Long blond hair whipped her face and breasts.

The crew couldn't take their eyes off of her. As if by magic, she would disappear into the ocean's blackness, then emerge as if flying with fish wings. Her silvery face was beautiful and her deep blue eyes sparkled like two jewels.

The siren's song became louder, drowning out the thunder. Now the Captain let go of the wheel to hold his hands over his ears. They were pounding with blood. Every sailor was bleeding from his ears! Her cold blue lips puckered into an evil smile as she attached herself to the mast. One look in her eyes, a sailor dies!

Like two steel knives, she gouged out each man's eyes. She was the "Medusa of the Sea". The mermaid screamed her Banshee song as the sailors fell one by one. Some jumped into the churning ocean just to escape the horrific sound.

Captain Smyth crumpled onto the ship's deck in a twisted ball. Closer and closer the ship veered toward the jagged rocks. With a mighty crash, the hull was split in

half. Those who didn't drown were savagely killed by the
mermaid's sharp fangs ripping apart their throats. Not
one man was spared.

   Voracious she was! After the storm passed, the sun
shone on a calm beautiful day. Another ship had been
destroyed by the mermaid's siren song. Another jeweled
scale sparkled brightly on her long flowing tail.

OLD MACDONALD HAD A FARM

"Old MacDonald had a farm,
E-I-E-I-O!"

And on that farm he had horses, cows, pigs, chickens, and goats. He also had a big rooster that crowed and "cock-a-doddle-dood" at the crack of dawn. Old man MacDonald and his wife didn't need an alarm clock!

Old MacDonald and his plump little wife lived on a farm far in the hills. The nearest neighbor was at least ten miles away. They liked it that way. Privacy was very important to them. If they needed supplies, Old man MacDonald and his plump little wife would take their rusty old pickup truck into town. That was at least a half day's ride just to get there. By the time they returned to their farm, it was time for dinner.

No one in town could remember ever seeing Old MacDonald selling any of his animals. He didn't even sell milk, cheese, or butter. They ate every animal on the farm, including the cranky old goats. Where did they get more animals? Most of them didn't reproduce because they just didn't have enough time.

You see, Old man MacDonald and his plump little wife were really witches in disguise. If anyone dared to enter their farmhouse, they never came out. Many lost souls would wander into the hill country just to be turned into pigs, cows, chickens, or goats.

The horses were saved for plowing. They didn't taste as good because their meat was too tough. If you were lucky enough to be turned into a chicken that laid lots of eggs, you might live a little longer. If you didn't produce, you ended up on a plate for Sunday dinner!

So, dear ones, don't wander into Old MacDonald's farm and ask for directions!

"E-I-E-I-O!"

MOTHER GOOSE BUMPS

Your goose is cooked, Mother Goose!

Mother Goose waddled along with her little goslings, all
ten strong.
"Hurry! Hurry! Don't dawdle when you waddle!"
They crossed the road, a tight family bunch,
"Let's get to the farmhouse for our lunch."

Farmer Fred laid out the corn, a very special treat.
"Come, Mother Goose and young ones,
I've got lots of food to eat!"
He counted ten of her babies as they lined up in a row,
"One day you'll all be big and fat,
Each one of you will grow."

Next day he counted only nine,
What happened to number ten?
Mother Goose said one got eaten by a big old nasty hen.
Every day Farmer Fred counted her goslings,
Another one dead!

Now there were only eight,
Who's been eating her goslings for their dinner plate?
When he counted only five,
Why didn't the others survive?

He asked dear Mother Goose one day,
She honked and squawked, began to pray.
"Not one survived. The old wolf is to blame!
He ate each one with long sharp teeth,
Indeed, it is a shame!"

Mother Goose was getting fat,
Feathers flew from her beak when she spat.
"I ate my babies, I confess,
They were so plump and yummy!"
She burped and wobbled out of sight with goslings in her
tummy.

BLACK WIDOW

What tangled webs we weave.
A giant spider licks her hungry lips with a sticky tongue,
Beware the Black Widow! She devours the weak and young!

She weaves her magic web with the blood of dying victims, helpless, imprisoned in strands of poisonous silk. She is ravenous, with an insatiable appetite.

Her web became so huge that it spread spidery fingers across large trees. It was a giant trap swaying in the wind. Nothing could penetrate or destroy it because it was BEWITCHED! Let me tell you the tale of how the Black Widow came to be.

Once there was a beautiful woman who fell in love with a handsome powerful king. They wed and had many children. Their great castle was nestled in the mountains.

Little did the queen know that her husband was in love with another woman. He grew cold and was very cruel to her and the children. When she asked him why he no longer loved her, he beat her mercilessly, imprisoning her and the children in the deep dark dungeon.

For years, they suffered at the hands of the king. No one knew they were kept prisoners because the king told his subjects they abandoned him and left the country. Not believable, but he got away with it because he was king. Who's going to challenge the king?

The queen put a curse on him and summoned the Dark Prince. He heard her pleas and came to her one night. He promised to destroy the king and his mistress,

Under one condition!

He wanted her soul. The queen was so desperate that she agreed to his offer. The next day the king and his lover were found dead in their royal bed, twisted and tortured in a most horrific way.

Nobody knew who murdered them, but they eventually found the queen and her children, releasing them from their captivity. She called upon the Dark Prince once again, begging him not to take her soul. Furious, the Dark Prince summoned all his evil forces and cast a powerful spell on her. She became the BLACK WIDOW.

He turned her into a hideous voracious spider. The cursed Black Widow ate her children and began to spin her web with their souls. She could hear their screams in the bloody silky threads. She was forever to be a vile creature, doomed to spin her magic web, devouring unsuspecting prey.

Be careful where you walk in the woods. The Black Widow's invisible web of poisonous silk will take your life!

And that, dear children, is how the Black Widow came to be. Sweet spidery dreams!

"BLACK WIDOW"

GOLDIE'S LOCKS

Did you ever hear of the little girl with long blond hair who stumbled upon a family of bears? In that fairy tale she survived. In this Scary Fairy's tale, well, read on dear ones.

Deep in the forest lived a family of bears. There was the "Papa", the "Mama", and the "Baby". These particular bears were very organized. Papa Bear foraged for food in the woods. Mama Bear did all the cooking. Baby Bear ate everything in sight. In fact, Baby Bear was always hungry.

The family even had their own "beds" to sleep in. Not exactly your typical beds. Their beds were supported by layers of bones for the base. The bones were layered with mulch, leaves, and various plants. This was covered tightly with a wrapping of stretchy material. This stretchy "cocoon" came in many colors. It was almost "skin-like", shall we say.

One afternoon, all three bears went on a family outing. Their cave was open in the front, so anyone could enter. That is, anyone stupid enough to venture into a bear cave.

It just so happened that a little girl with long blond hair was lost in the woods. Her name was "Goldie Locks" because she had such beautiful golden locks of hair flowing down her back. Why she was alone in the forest is anyone's guess. But, let's not wander too far down the path.

Goldie Locks came upon the cave and was curious to see where it led. She was also very hungry and tired. So, upon entering the bear cave, she found neat little piles of meat stacked in three rows. She sampled the first chunk of meat. Too chewy!

The second slab was too raw for her taste. She tossed it aside. The third little cube of meat was just right. Medium rare. So, Goldie Locks ate all of that.

Being very tired, she proceeded to wander far back into the cave and found three "beds". She had to try out all of those, of course. The first bed was very large. She sunk into it and was almost swallowed whole!

The second bed was medium sized but didn't feel right. Somehow the stretchy covering was a bit too rough, not smooth and pink like the smaller one.

So, Goldie Locks climbed into Baby Bear's cot and snuggled into it. Yes, the smooth pink stretchy covering was just right. She fell into a deep sleep.

Finally, after a few hours, the three bears came home. Something was amiss. It smelled like a human! Papa Bear was furious that his meat had been bitten into. Mama Bear knew something was wrong when she saw that her raw meat was tossed aside. Baby Bear growled because his was all eaten. He was so hungry!

The three bears lumbered into the bedroom cave. Sniffing around his bed, Papa Bear was very angry to see an imprint in his stretchy covering. Mama Bear knew something was wrong with hers when she smelled a human scent. Baby Bear came upon Goldie Locks sleeping peacefully in his cot. Being very hungry, he bit into Goldie and ripped her arm off. She screamed and screamed and screamed!

∽

Finally, she stopped screaming. There was almost nothing left of poor Goldie. Baby Bear had eaten almost every bit of her.

Papa Bear and Mama Bear were relieved. They tossed her bones aside and began gathering what was left of her pink flesh for the next "stretchy covering". Goldie's golden locks would make a nice addition too.

Baby Bear was getting a new bed!

THREE LITTLE PIGGIES

There once was a little town called "Hogsville". It was right smack in the middle of "Wolfsbane" and "Butcher's Block". In this tiny town of Hogsville were three little piggies. They all lived in the same hut made of straw. Why?

It was strong, mixed with hairs of their little chinny chin chins. You see, pigs have very coarse hair which is useful when building straw houses.

They needed to be protected from the wolves in Wolfsbane and Butcher's Block. Wolves loved bacon, pork chops, and ham. Anything relating to pigs made them salivate and very vicious. They sharpened their fangs, anticipating the "Three Little Piggies Buffet".

When the wind was right, the scent of the three piggies wafted through the air. This drove the wolves to the brink of insanity! One night they formed a pack and surrounded Hogsville, trapping the three little piggies in their straw hut.

Little did the wolves know that the hut was fenced in with the long strands of the hairs from their chinny chin chins. Only the Alpha Male got through. Never mess with three angry piggies!

After killing the Alpha, they ate his insides. What a wolfie mess! All three piggies crawled inside his huge hairy wolf body and left Hogsville with the wolf pack following.

⤳

They led them into a swamp of quicksand. Every single wolf was swallowed by the wet sticky sand pits. The three piggies shed Alpha's body and cried "Wee, Wee, Wee" all the way home.

They now live peacefully in a big brick house made of pork rinds from piggy toes and the hairs of their chinny chin chins. Occasionally you can hear them snorting and howling at the moon.

Be careful never to cry "WOLF"!

CINDY

The Real Story of Cinderella

"And they lived happily ever after". No they didn't! To tell the truth, it was a horrific marriage. Cindy was not the beautiful perfect person created in that fairy tale. She came from the cinders, remember?

Cindy had dust on her face all the time. The cinders were cruel reminders of where she came from. She was a gutter snipe.

Children, do you want to hear the truthful story? You might not like it, but Scary Fairy wants to tell it anyway. Nestle in your little beds and listen to the tale of the real Cinderella.

Ella was a poor peasant girl who was taken in by a wealthy family as a maid. This family had a mother, father, and two daughters. When Ella came into their lives, it turned the peaceful home into domestic chaos. At first, Ella was demure and quite charming. That was her disguise.

Cleaning the large fireplace was one of her tasks. Cinders would fly into her face and hair when she swept them out of the hearth. So, they would all laugh, and eventually the name "Cinderella" stuck. She didn't like that one bit.

"Call me Cindy if you like, but not Cinderella!" She

would scream and run into her room at the end of the house. This was the maid's quarters.

The mother and two daughters always made Cindy bring them their breakfast in bed. She despised them. One morning Cindy spied a box of rat poison on the shelf. This was powerful poison used to kill the huge rats running around the property.

Well, guess what Cindy did? Yes, that's right, children. She poured rat poison in their morning "grog" (that was really strong tea). All three drank the poisonous brew. All three died horribly. The father was out riding in the countryside and had no clue what was happening.

When he came home, he found the three dead women in their bedrooms, faces twisted in torment. Where was Cindy? She was hysterical crying in the kitchen. Panicking, she told the story (all lies) of an old woman who knocked on the door and gave her a bag of "tea leaves" to try. Cindy said she didn't know they were tainted with rat poison and that the old woman was really a wicked witch. Now, who would believe that story? He did.

In those days, witches were everywhere. Just look at Snow White. But that's another story. When they buried the mother and daughters, Cindy moved right in and assumed the role of "wife".

No fairy Godmother here. No pumpkins turning into coaches, no ball at the castle, and definitely no Prince Charming. They eventually married, but it was a disaster. Cindy was wicked and wanted the huge estate for herself. She hated the husband and would scream and carry on all the time. She refused to sleep with him. We won't go into details on that subject, children.

One morning, Cindy decided she had enough. Yes, you're right, kiddies. Rat poison! Into his morning "grog" she poured a big spoonful of poison. Another one gone! She buried him in the plot next to the wife and daughters. Claiming he passed away from a heart attack, Cindy became a very rich widow.

Nobody questioned any of their deaths. In those days, people were too busy fighting infidels or arranging social events like masquerade balls at the castle. Oh, one other thing I forgot to mention, children.

Cindy did go to the ball at the castle wearing her famous glass slippers. Prince Charming fell in love with her and they married, against the wishes of the King and Queen and the whole town.

They did not live happily ever after. The last piece of news anyone heard was the Prince was very ill. On his death bed he complained his "grog" tasted funny.

Cindy was a very, very naughty girl.

DON'T GO DOWN
TO THE BASEMENT!

Rattle, rattle, rattle! The door knob was turning frantically on the basement door. Thank goodness it was locked because who knows what evil lurked behind it? Violently shaking, the pounding finally stopped. A word of warning, dear ones:

Don't go down to the basement!

Little Alice was crying,
Her face was deathly white.
What could be hiding in the basement that night?
Eyes as big as saucers,
She stared at the basement door.
Something tried getting in,
Alice hit the floor.

She fainted with an awful thud,
Her parents yelled and screamed.
The door knob rattled and shook again
for an eternity, it seemed.

Next day the house was quiet,
Alice took a chance.
She slowly opened the basement door,
wetting her underpants!

Shaking like a little leaf,
she tiptoed down the stairs.
Creak, creak, they began to squeak,
"Come out, if anyone dares!"

The air smelled stale and very thick,
Alice began feeling sick.
She peered into the dark and gloom,
A shadow ran across the room!

"Who's there?" She screamed and turned to run,
but something grabbed her leg.
Under the stairs she heard a growl,
"Don't hurt me, please, I beg!"

It pulled her down the basement stairs,
Red eyes glowed in the dark.
Scratched and bitten, she was a mess,
The demon left its mark.

Crawling up the stairs, poor Alice was a sight,
She never made it to the top,
They say she died of fright!

Beware the demon under the stairs,
It will shake you to your core.
Rattle, rattle, rattle, rattle,
Lock the basement door!

THE BATHTUB

Little ones, are you afraid to get into the bathtub alone? You will be after you read this scary tale!

Shivering with fear, Penny stared at the huge drain swallowing her bath water. It was spinning like a nasty whirlpool. She cringed in the corner of the tub, afraid she would be next.

Screaming for her mother, Penny clawed at the sides of the tub, slipping towards the drain that would swallow her. Swirling faster, louder, the water made a powerful sucking noise. She felt something licking her toes.

It wrapped its slimy tongue around her leg. Suck, suck, suck! Half of her tiny body was dragged through the drain. Where was her mother? Screaming bloody murder, (that's exactly what it was), she disappeared down the hungry mouth.

There was no trace of dear sweet Penny except a few strands of blond hair. It was a grim discovery for her mother, indeed. What a shame!

Parents, never leave your children alone in the bathtub. There's something very wicked down there!

AUNT MARTHA'S KITCHEN

Aunt Martha was a wonderful cook. The smell of freshly baked cookies would waft through the house. She was known far and wide for her award-winning pies. Apple pies, blueberry pies, cherry pies, any kind of pie you can imagine.

Yes, Aunt Martha was "Queen of the Cuisine". Everyone wanted to know how she made them, but Aunt Martha was very secretive. Nobody knew her recipes because she was protective of her "ingredients".

One day, a newspaper boy rang her doorbell. He asked for payment for the last three weeks because Aunt Martha was behind in her bills. She claimed she was broke and didn't have a penny to her name. That's what she told him. Of course, Aunt Martha was lying through her teeth. And what teeth she had!

The poor little newsboy never had a chance. Her long sharp fangs came out as she lunged toward him. Grabbing him by the neck, she sunk her teeth into his throat and ripped him apart. Oh, so young and fresh, he would make a tasty mince meat pie. Too bad he was so small. She had just enough of him to bake a fairly decent size pie.

Ah, the aromas in her kitchen were amazing! Through the open windows neighbors could smell her pies, anticipating more award-winning masterpieces.

Don't ever ring Aunt Martha's doorbell. She might ask you in and serve you a nice hot bowl of "chicken" noodle soup. The only problem is, those aren't noodles. They wiggle and squirm around the bowl. WORMS! The ones that don't wiggle are from, well, it's a "no-brainer".

"Slurp, slurp, down the hatch! I think I'll make another batch!" Yes, Aunt Martha was quite a gourmet cook. No reservations needed. You could be the "Catch of the Day".

Why are her chocolate chip cookies winking at me?

THE LEGEND
OF THE SEA WOLF

He was known as "Sea Wolf", a submariner who prowled the seas. Like a phantom, he blended with the gray walls and decks of the submarine. He was elusive. He was also dead.

"Clang, clang", the bell rang as the submarine prepared to dive into the cold black sea. Rough waves pounded the sides of the old sub, defying it to enter its watery domain.

Down, down, the submarine sank deeper, hitting bottom. This was war time, and being undetected was crucial. Sitting silently on the ocean floor like a giant fish waiting to catch its prey, it blended with the sea's murky camouflage.

The crew was nervous. Sweat ran down their faces, not daring to make a sound. Pinging noises came from the sonar detector. An enemy sub was nearby, searching for them.

Then something went terribly wrong. Lights in the sub began to flicker and a nauseating odor filled the air. It smelled like death. The rotting stench became unbearable. Everyone was choking from the horrific smell.

A huge black mass formed on the ceiling of the sub, slithering along the walls. It was the Sea Wolf! The men began to panic, running from the main cabin, trying to escape the menacing Sea Wolf's deadly grasp.

The Captain grabbed his pistol and shot at the enormous black mass. The Sea Wolf consumed him, until there was nothing left but bare bones. The carnage continued. Not one man survived.

Silence. As quickly as he appeared, the Sea Wolf dissipated into a black mist.

On the enemy sub, the crew was on edge. Something wasn't right. There was a horrific odor permeating the cabin.

It smelled like death.

LITTLE RED

Little Red wore a hooded red riding cape. Simply stated, she was "Little Red Riding Hood". That's all she wore. Every day, the same outfit. So, we'll just call her "Little Red".

Her grandmother lived in a small cottage in the woods. Why she chose to live in the middle of a forest is quite a mystery. Grandma was old and feeble, relying on Little Red to bring her food and help her around the cottage.

We don't really know where Little Red lived. If she had parents, wouldn't they help her with grandma? But let's not over think this fairy tale.

Also living in the woods was a nasty old wolf. He loved the smell of grandma and he also sniffed around for Little Red. When she was skipping through the forest with her basket of goodies, he would hide behind trees, drooling through his long sharp fangs. The old wolf was waiting for the right moment to devour her.

Little Red knew she was being followed. She wasn't stupid. You see, she really wasn't really innocent and helpless. Under that hood were two horns growing out of her head. She was actually a demon.

Grandma wasn't feeble either. An old witch in disguise, she had ways to make curious visitors disappear. There was always someone brewing in her big black cauldron (a huge cast iron pot).

One afternoon, Little Red went skipping through the woods carrying her basket of goodies. The hungry wolf decided it was time to eat her. He was losing patience and was starving. He pounced on Little Red as she came around the bend. She pulled off her hood and gored him with her horns. Reaching inside her basket, she pulled out a huge knife. Slicing the wolf's throat, she carved him into little pieces, filling her basket to the brim. Ah, fresh wolf meat!

Grandma was smiling when Little Red came in. She had the big black pot boiling.

My, what a big appetite you have, Grandma!

RAPUNZEL

"Rapunzel, Rapunzel, let down your hair!"
(This is the very short version of a ridiculous fairy tale)

Rapunzel lived in a tower. Her father kept her prisoner because he didn't want her to meet men. How deliciously wicked! Rapunzel never cut her blond hair, so it grew very, very long and heavy. It was so heavy that she dragged it around the small room. Exhausting!

One day, she had a visitor. Yes, a handsome prince just happened to be nearby in the forest and heard her crying. Well, that was all he needed. Climbing up the tower was impossible, but when Rapunzel came to the window, she had a brilliant idea. Why not lower her long heavy hair down the tower so the prince could climb up and rescue her?

When he scaled up her hair, pulling on it mercilessly, he climbed through the window and into her room. Now they were both stuck! How did they get down?

That version is total nonsense. Rapunzel had short hair. She cut her tresses every day, making a long braided rope from those golden locks. Quite ingenious! For years, Rapunzel secretively wove her long strands into a knotted "ladder". It was a very high tower, you see.

When she dropped her braided hair to the ground, she anchored the top to the latticed window. Rapunzel climbed down and ran off with a man who just happened to be riding his horse in the forest. He was no Prince, however.

~~

When Rapunzel's father found out she escaped from the tower, he sent a search party to look for her. She was never found.

Rapunzel dyed her blond hair brown, kept it short, married the man on the horse and had two children. Their names were Hansel and Gretel.

But that's another fairy tale, children.

HANSEL AND GRETEL

The Children of Rapunzel

Now that you know the real Rapunzel, this is the story of her two children, Hansel and Gretel. Forget the fairy tale you heard before. Trust me.

Hansel was a bright handsome boy. His blue eyes sparkled in the sun and blond curls framed his face in a most angelic way. Some folks swore they could see a halo over his head.

Gretel, on the other hand, had freckles all over her face. She was a spunky fiery red head. A real "Tom Boy". They were inseparable.

Hansel and Gretel lived in a simple cottage with their mother Rapunzel and father Yohan. They were a happy family, always taking long walks in the woods, except in certain parts of the forest. Rapunzel and Yohan warned Hansel and Gretel never to walk in the "Forbidden Forest", because a particularly evil witch lived there. She lured unsuspecting children to her candy house. Then she ate them. She had a huge oven just for that purpose.

Hearing this, Hansel vowed never to enter the "Forbidden Forest". Gretel wrinkled her freckled nose and laughed. She didn't believe a word of it.

One lovely summer day, Gretel suggested to Hansel

they should go for a walk in the woods. She wanted to venture into the witch's "Forbidden Forest" and see the candy house for herself. Hansel was frightened, warning her that it was dangerous and a very bad idea. Gretel won.

Together, they approached the beautiful house, awed by tempting desserts and candy decorating the outside. The aromas wafting out of the witch's candy house were too tempting to ignore. Besides, they were both hungry.

Gretel was the first one to snatch a sweet dessert from the window sill. Hansel grabbed a gingerbread man, devouring it in seconds. The two continued their glutinous meal of cookies, candy and anything else they could stuff in their mouths.

Soon Hansel collapsed on the stoop made of chocolate sprinkles. Gretel held her stomach and rolled her eyes. She was feeling sick. She actually had a green tinge to her face.

The door of the candy house opened. There stood the witch. "Have enough sweets, my sweet children?" She cackled.

Hansel screamed when he saw the wrinkled old hag hovering over them. Gretel tried to speak but couldn't get a word out. The candy was taking its toll and both of them froze in fear.

The witch dragged Gretel by her hair and pulled on Hansel's leg, tossing them like dolls into her kitchen.

"Such delicious children you are! I'll have a feast tonight!" With that, she grabbed a long stick and lit it with a lick of her slithering black tongue. The oven was huge, just the right size for two children. She placed the flaming stick into the oven.

～～

Hansel and Gretel were tied into neat little bundles, sprinkled with the witch's favorite seasonings and basted with her special oils. She stuffed their mouths with a wicked concoction of mashed tongues and lips from other children's body parts. She never wasted anything.

When the oven was the right temperature, she carefully placed the two side by side into the glowing embers. By now, Hansel and Gretel passed out and maybe dead before they even hit the flames.

Yes, the old witch had a feast that night. Nothing was left of poor Hansel and Gretel. Not one freckle, not one blond hair. In this fairy tale they did not escape. The witch was not the one thrown into the oven, just two curious children who wandered too far into the "Forbidden Forest".

Rapunzel's hair turned white from fright when she learned of their fates. Yohan tried to burn down the witch's candy house, but nothing could destroy it because it was protected by a powerful spell.

To this day, it still stands. Be careful, dear ones, when you stroll through the woods. Don't dare go for a walk in the witch's forest. It might be your last!

SNOW WHITE

Her face was white as snow. Do you know why, children? She was an Albino. That's right. "Snow" also had a slight pinkish color around her eyes. Her pupils were red. Of course, in the fairy tale we all know, Snow was just a normal girl growing up in a castle with a wicked Queen who was jealous of her.

Why would she be jealous of an Albino? Anyway, the Queen was also a witch. One day, Snow had enough of the Queen's ridicule about her red eyes and translucent skin. She ran away.

In those days, the only place to hide was the forest. There were lots of forests in the vast countryside. It was easy for Snow to disappear. She wandered into a clearing in the woods, coming upon a cute little cottage. Little did she know that seven little men (also known as dwarfs) lived there. Scary thought, but let's continue.

Snow knocked on the door. No one answered, so she opened it. What a tidy cottage! She was so exhausted that she plopped into one of the tiny beds. Her feet dangled off the foot of the cot, but she made herself comfortable anyway.

It was dusk and the seven dwarfs were on their way home from the diamond mines. "Hi Ho, Hi Ho! Back home we go!"

Snow woke up upon hearing their singing, startling the

dwarfs. They immediately were awed and quite frightened when they saw her red eyes and shimmering white skin. After hearing her sad story, all seven decided she could stay and live with them. Snow was overjoyed and danced around the room. She was a very good dancer.

The problem was, where was she going to sleep? She was too big to fit into a small cot, so they built her a normal size bed. Dwarfs work quickly.

The next morning at dawn, they gathered their pickaxes to work in the diamond mines. What did they do with all those diamonds? We won't go into that now. Singing their song, "Hi Ho, Hi Ho! It's off to work we go!" the cheerful seven left the cottage.

Snow busied herself around the house. Suddenly, there was a knock at the door. An old hag stood outside, holding a big red apple. Snow took the apple and bit into it. The old witch cackled, disappearing in the forest. Of course, we know who the old witch was, don't we? Yes, it was the wicked Queen.

Snow immediately fell into a coma. When the dwarfs returned, they found her lying on the floor. Panicking, all seven tried to bring her back to life, but nothing worked.

Thinking she was dead, they buried her in the back yard.

When Snow opened her eyes, she was six feet under. Clawing at the coffin, she screamed and screamed until she ran out of air.

Sorry, children! You'll never look at apples the same way again.

SLEEPING BEAUTY

On "Invitation Etiquette": Keep your friends close and your enemies closer. Always invite the Wicked Witch!"

The King and Queen made a horrible mistake. A huge "Faux Pas", shall we say. When it comes to inviting guests to your newborn daughter's christening at the castle, don't forget the most powerful evil witch in the kingdom. MALEFICENT!

She was snubbed. Can we blame her for getting all pissy and out of sorts when she didn't receive a special invitation to the royal affair? When it comes to curses and spells, Maleficent was the master. She should have been the first one on the Royal Invitation List. This was going to cost them dearly.

Aurora was a beautiful baby, blessed by three Fairy Godmothers. Why wouldn't she be radiant and talented? When Maleficent crashed the party, she cursed Aurora and the royal family, casting the "Mother of All Spells". In those days, if a powerful witch loses her cool, you'd better take it seriously.

As the story goes, Aurora was to prick her finger on a spinning wheel's needle on her 16th birthday, falling into a deep sleep until awakened by a true love's kiss.

That part is true, children. Aurora did prick her finger on a spinning wheel's sharp needle. She fell into a very deep sleep for a long time. In fact, she slept for over 50 years before a Prince found her. She was still beautiful in her glass coffin. Maleficent made sure of that.

But here's where the wicked twist comes in. The truth is, when the Prince opened her glass coffin to kiss her, all of that pure magical air keeping Aurora young and beautiful evaporated, leaving her exposed to the elements.

As soon as the Prince kissed her on the lips, her face started to shrivel into wrinkles and scabs. Aurora's beautiful long auburn hair turned white. She even sported a few hairs on her chin. When she opened her eyes, all she saw was a handsome young man staring at her in horror. Our dear Prince Charming took off like a scared rabbit, jumped on his horse and was never seen again.

Oh, Magnificent Maleficent! You are a deliciously wicked one! Payback is a bitch.

THE HEEBIE GEEBIE MAN

Dat man give me da heebie geebies!
He roams around da house quiet as a mouse,
Sneakin' up on me like a shadow.
Swayin' back and forth like der's a hurricane a'blowin',
Wit a grin on his face,
He got two glassy eyes a'glowin'.
Yep, dat man give me da heebie geebies,
Fer sure, he gonna git me one day!

Deep in Bayou Country, there's a legend about The Heebie Geebie Man. He haunts the steamy swamps at night, a restless soul. Don't dare venture out if you want to live, my sweet children! Let me spin a tale for you about The Heebie Geebie Man.

He was a mean old Cajun, born in the heart of Louisiana's Bayous. Before he died alone in his barren cabin, he cursed anyone who entered his black swamps. A Voodoo man, dark witch was he. Dead chickens hung from his front door, bled dry. He would pluck their feathers, mixed with blood and strange potions to use in his Black Magic rituals. If someone had the bad luck to wander into his swampy home, he would never live to tell about it.

No one knows how he died, but they say he became one of the "undead", a zombie. Wandering the swamps, he would eat raw gator meat. Glassy-eyed, mouth open wide, wailing and moaning on a full moon, The Heebie Geebie Man was one with the Devil.

Sinking into quicksand ponds that were hidden behind tall weeds, The Heebie Geebie Man was devoured by the voracious sand. He would crawl out of the slime, clawing at the earth with rotting black hands. When you're the walking dead, nothing can kill you. That was his curse.

Keep the lights on when you go to bed, children. The Heebie Geebie Man lives in the dark and doesn't like the morning light either. He sleeps in his swampy Bayou, waiting for the moon to shine.

In your nightmares, little ones, remember the song:

"Beware da Heebie Geebie Man. Fer sure he gonna git you one day!"

ITCHY GOOMY

Remember the tale of Itchy Goomy who sucked her thumb constantly? This is what happens to children who suck their thumbs and don't listen to their mother.

Itchy Goomy (Itchy Gums) would suck her thumb so much that she pushed her front teeth forward. That's called "Buck-toothed". Not very attractive.

Itchy was very "Buck-toothed". She continued to suck her thumb anyway. No matter what her mother did, Itchy didn't listen. Her front teeth jutted out so far that she couldn't eat properly.

Mother tried everything. She dipped her thumb in iodine, wrapped it in a bandage soaked in bleach, tied her hands behind her back. Nothing worked. Itchy was hooked.

One day, her mother was so frustrated she took a big carving knife from the kitchen and threatened to cut off Itchy's thumb. Well, Itchy laughed and started sucking with a vengeance. Mother grabbed her hand, slammed it on the table and spread her fingers apart. She whacked off her thumb. It rolled on the floor, blood spurting everywhere. Itchy's face turned white with horror.

She screamed and ran toward her bloody thumb. Picking it up, Itchy tried putting it back on her hand, but it was too late. She was hysterical. Mother wrapped Itchy's hand with bandages, wiped the blood off the table and placed her thumb in a jar. This was a sick reminder for Itchy never to suck the other thumb.

∼∾∼

It didn't work. Itchy defiantly started sucking on her thumb. Guess what happened, dear ones? Now there were two thumbs in the jar.

Itchy began sucking on her fingers. One by one, Mother whacked them off with her big carving knife. Eventually, Itchy had no fingers left. Mother had to buy a bigger jar to fit all ten fingers.

So, children, if you ever have a desire to suck your thumb, remember the tale of Itchy Goomy.

Thank you, Mommy!

JACK AND
HIS BEANS TALK

Do you believe in magic beans? Let me tell you a story.

Jack was a dull-witted boy. Why his mother sent him on an errand to sell a cow is beyond me. Jack was given one simple task and he blew it.

Jack and his mother were poor. His mother needed money, so she started selling her animals and anything else she could spare. One day, she sent Jack into town to sell her old cow. This cow wasn't worth much. In fact, it was worth beans.

Jack was ripe for the picking. He was offered three "magic beans" in exchange for his cow. Mother really wanted cash, but Jack was an idiot and took the beans instead. What did he do next? Yes, children, he ate them.

Now, these beans were no ordinary beans. They were powerful drugs. Soon Jack began hallucinating. He imagined all sorts of weird and strange things, especially giants and a beanstalk that grew into a huge tree, shaking the ground like an earthquake. Jack was tripping.

He was found in a farmer's field screaming about a giant trying to eat him and a goose that laid golden eggs.

"Fee Fi Fo Fum!" Jack kept yelling. Well, children, the

villagers didn't know what to do with this crazy boy, so they tied him to a tree and let him rant and rave for two days.

～

Finally, Jack was so exhausted he fell asleep. After the drugs wore off, he went home empty-handed. His mother was furious. She sent him away to an asylum where he spent the rest of his days telling odd stories about a beanstalk that grew so big you could climb it to the Land of Giants in the sky.

Oh dear.

Little ones, when your mother sends you on an errand, please stick to the plan. Definitely don't eat the "magic beans".

Fee Fi Fo Fum!

THE WITCH
WITH A TWITCH

There once was a witch with a nervous twitch,
Her bony fingers shook as she gave a wicked look.
She cast a crooked spell from the pit of fire and hell,
Beware of the witch with a wicked twitch!

Children, do you know how the Crooked Man became crooked? The next time you recite that little rhyme, you might look over your shoulder to see if the witch with a twitch is standing behind you, cackling with an evil smile through crooked teeth and lizard's skin.

I DARE YOU!

Let me spin a tale of the Crooked Man. We'll get to Humpty Dumpty later. Hubert was a miserable old man. He lived by himself in a tiny house in the quaint English countryside. He had a cat and a mouse in the house. Why the cat never ate the mouse is truly a mystery.

Hubert also had money hidden under his mattress. He didn't believe in banks, so he always carried six pence in his wallet when he needed it. One day Hubert came upon an old woman who looked like a beggar. She had a tin cup in her hand and claimed she was blind. Hubert ignored her because he was an old miser and very selfish. He didn't believe in helping people, especially giving money to blind old hags.

The old woman clinked and clanked her money cup in front of him, waiving her cane in the dirt road. Hubert knew she was blind, so he snatched the cup from her and pushed her to the ground.

∽

Well, that was a big mistake! You see, dear little ones, this was no ordinary old woman. This was the wicked witch with a twitch. She slowly got to her feet, turned around to face Hubert, and with a twisted grin pointed a bony finger at him. Shaking violently, she cursed him and turned Hubert into a Crooked Man (because he was crooked anyway). His body bent in all directions. It was quite a bizarre sight to behold! She cursed his house, his cat and his mouse. She even cursed his money hidden under the mattress.

The witch twitched and bitched, moaned and groaned. Hubert lay in a crooked heap in the dirt road. When he crookedly limped back to his house, he was horrified at the sight. His house was as crooked as he was! A crooked cat and mouse ran out of the house. With a crooked "Meow", it wobbled and hobbled. The crooked mouse ate a piece of crooked cheese and began to sneeze. Little pieces of crooked six pence went up its nose and killed the poor crooked creature.

See what happens when you steal from a blind old beggar woman? The wicked witch with a twitch went on down the dirt road and spied a huge egg sitting on a brick wall. But that's another story, children.

HUMPTY DUMPTY
(Walking on Eggshells)

"Humpty Dumpty sat on a wall,
Humpty Dumpty had a great fall."

Now, why would an egg sit on a wall? Another strange nursery rhyme, children. But let's not put all our eggs in one basket.

When the witch with a twitch came upon Humpty, she couldn't believe her eyes. "Well, what do we have here?" She cackled, pointing her bony finger at the frightened egg.

He began shaking with fear. "Please don't make me fall off this wall. I'll crack in a million pieces!"

The witch eyed Humpty hungrily. "I think I'd like scrambled eggs for dinner!" With that, she twitched with all her might. What a terrible sight! Humpty felt the wall shake. The earth began to quake. He held on with all his might, but knew it was a losing fight. His insides boiled and rattled uncontrollably as the witch twitched and turned, dancing around the wall. Her black tongue slithered in and out like a serpent.

Poor Humpty! Eventually, he fell with a loud "CRACK!" Tiny bits and pieces scattered all over the ground. Humpty was scrambled. The old witch gathered scrambled Humpty in her sack and hobbled away. She was going to have a delicious dinner tonight!

Little ones, the next time you have scrambled eggs, remember poor Humpty and say a prayer. He's in that big omelet in the sky!

RING AROUND THE ROSIE

"Ring around the rosie,
A pocket full of posies,
Ashes, ashes, we all fall down!"

That nauseating rhyme. Dear little ones, do you know what that really means? How you dance around and fall to the ground laughing. Scary Fairy will wipe the smiles off your sweet little faces after you read my story.

A long, long time ago, there were many ships sailing into ports carrying big nasty black rats. Yes, the ones that resemble small dogs. Well, children, these nasty rats brought disease into the towns and cities. Eventually, it became so bad they called it the Black Death, or the Bubonic Plague. Millions of people died in a most horrific way. This will give you nightmares, but let's continue anyway, sweet ones.

First, your face will turn a swollen reddish rosy color followed by big blisters and oozing welts. It's almost how a really ugly witch looks when she's angry. I won't mention all the other disgusting symptoms that follow, but eventually you die and they throw you in a huge pile in the streets with all the other corpses. So, "Ashes, ashes, we all fall down" is really what that means. Death, children. The Black Death.

Pick the posies to ward off the horrible stench. What pretty little flowers they are! Put them all in your pocket and dance around in a ring. I hate to spoil your fun, but the next time you want to sing and dance to that disgusting song, remember what it really means.

Sorry to ruin your childhood.

THE PRINCESS
AND THE PEA

Ah, the test of royalty! How cruel. Does one have to bleed Royal Blue or bruise easily? One "princess" was so sensitive she could feel a little pea under ten mattresses. Now, that's either very impressive or downright scary. If it was up to Scary Fairy, I'd place giant cockroaches or slithering snakes under each mattress and see how well she sleeps. But that's just my wicked sense of humor. What really happened to our dear little princess?

Once upon a very, very long time in a very, very small kingdom, there was a very, very tiny "Princess in Waiting". She wasn't a princess yet, just waiting for the Royal Test to see if she really had "Royal Blood". In those medieval days, they had nothing to measure how royal you were, so they invented strange ways to weed out "peasant blood" from tainting the Royals.

One day, a basket was left by the gates of the castle. The King and Queen couldn't afford to dig a moat, so they had iron gates built to protect them from infidels. Anyway, a guard spotted the basket. When he opened it, there was a baby girl sleeping peacefully under a pink blanket. Well, he immediately brought the baby to the King and Queen.

"What do we do with this baby girl?" The King bellowed. The Queen was touched by this sweet little bundle. She wanted to adopt her on the spot. The King was very wary and didn't want to take any chances that the baby was from a poor peasant family and would infect them with her unpleasant "peasant-ness". Is that a word? Needless to say, the Queen won. The Queen always wins.

～

Years went by, until the King announced that he wanted to test the young girl to see how royally sensitive she was. So, he piled up ten mattresses and placed a pea under the bottom one. If the girl could "feel" the pea, she was indeed a Royal. Ridiculous, yes, but the Queen agreed to the "Pea Test".

One night, the "princess" fell asleep on top of the huge pile of mattresses. After a while, she tossed and turned so violently that she rolled off the bed of ten mattresses and crashed to the stone floor. Bruised and bleeding, she ran screaming down the castle halls until the King and Queen woke up in horror.

Thinking the "princess" was injured by the pea under ten mattresses, this would prove beyond a doubt that she was a "Royal". Idiots.

Eventually, they officially announced her as a Royal Princess. She was so sensitive they gave her the position as "Royal Mattress Tester", rating mattresses in the kingdom for quality and durability.

So, dear children, this is how the names "Queen" and "King" mattresses came to be, thanks to the princess and her pea.

PETER RABBIT

Rabbits, bunnies, so cute and cuddly, except when they eat everything in your cabbage patch. Cabbage, carrots, lettuce, anything growing in the farmer's field was a huge buffet for Peter Rabbit. Of course, he had help. Brothers, sisters, cousins, all destroying the farmer's crops.

That's what my next tale (or tail) is about, dear little darlings. Yes, Peter Rabbit. He was the leader of the Rabbit Pack. When Farmer Olsen noticed three of his huge cabbages were missing, he became very angry.

"I think it's Peter and his gang eating my cabbages!" He growled and stomped back to the farm house. Two nights later, Peter and his hungry relatives devoured another patch of lettuce, carrots and cabbages.

Farmer Olsen was furious! "How do I catch them in the act? Should I build a chicken wire fence? Maybe I should get a guard dog." He was desperate.

"Aha! I'll lay rabbit traps in the field!" So, Farmer Olsen placed traps in between the rows of vegetables. Next morning, another batch of cabbages disappeared! Peter and his hungry gang managed to avoid the traps and continued to wreak havoc in the farmer's field.

"I'll sprinkle a mixture of hot peppercorns and tobacco sauce on my crops. Surely, that will make them sick and they'll leave me alone!"

It just so happens that rabbits love that stuff and the banquet continued. By now, Peter and his gang were getting very fat. They ate so much that it became harder to hop around and move quickly in the night.

Farmer Olsen was ready. He cocked his rifle, waiting under the stars and full moon. He was going to kill every single one of those furry intruders. Sure enough, waddling towards the cabbage patch (what was left of it), were Peter and his hungry band of thieves.

BANG! BANG! Shots rang out. One by one, they dropped dead. The fur was flying, shall we say. Farmer Olsen killed every single rabbit. He gathered them up in a big sack and headed back to the house.

The next evening, there was a wonderful aroma coming from the farm house kitchen. Boiling away in a big pot was a most delicious rabbit stew!

So, kiddies, the next time you ask your parents for a cute little bunny as a pet, remember the story of Peter Rabbit.

Rabbit stew, anyone?

THREE BLIND MICE

"Three blind mice, three blind mice,
See how they run, see how they run!
They all ran after a farmer's wife,
Who cut off their tails with a carving knife,
Did you ever see such a sight in your life,
As three blind mice."

Disgusting. Cutting off their tails? Why were they blind? Another sick nursery rhyme children sing, not knowing the real story.

Did you ever hear of the wicked Mary Queen of England? She was also called "Bloody Mary". Mary didn't like Protestants. The Queen wanted everyone to become a Catholic, just like her. When you're Queen of England, you can demand anything you want and expect complete obedience from your subjects.

You have to understand in those stormy days, religion ruled kingdoms. Bloody Mary certainly earned her name. She actually loved bonfires. Lots of Protestants make for really good bonfires. Let's not dwell on that scenario, children.

There just so happened to be three very important Protestant leaders who defied Mary's orders to become Catholic. Mary was not pleased. She had them arrested and tortured. The three "mice" were blinded, then beheaded with a "carving knife", which really meant the Ax Man. Heads were rolling, shall we say.

The good old Ax Man was never out of a job. To add insult to injury, Bloody Mary had the three blind and headless men burned in the town square. Not a very pleasant sight to see.

Eventually, Bloody Mary got what she deserved. She was overthrown and publicly beheaded. Yes, by the same Ax Man. He had no loyalty to royalty. It appeared Mary was no longer the "Head of England".

When you're singing your hymns in church or going to Bible study, my little ones, remember how lucky you are. At least you don't have to face the Ax Man..for now.

Amen.

LONDON BRIDGE

"London Bridge is falling down,
Falling down, falling down,
London Bridge is falling down,
My fair lady.
Take the key and lock her up,
Lock her up, lock her up,
Take the key and lock her up,
My fair lady."

There was a bridge in London Town
that kept a secret dark.
"Inside are children buried!"
The townsfolk did remark.

To keep it from collapsing, bones made it strong,
Locked up until they died, 'twas said,
In the bridge they all belong.

My dear "Fair Lady", who were you?
The Queen who bled a "Royal Blue"?
What the hell was wrong with you?
My Fair Lady.

Sweet ones, dance and sing your song,
Hold your arms up high.
Remember what it really means,
The children all must die.

If you were the chosen ones,
Locked up in dark and gloom,
You'd never see the light of day,
imprisoned in a room.

London Bridge will never fall,
It's built with children's bones.
A tribute to the King and Queen,
Smiling on their thrones.

ROCK-A-BYE BABY

"Rock-A-Bye baby, on the treetops,
When the wind blows, the cradle will rock,
When the bough breaks, the cradle will fall,
And down will come baby, cradle and all."

If you want to murder your child, just put it in a cradle way up high on the treetops during a wicked storm. For sure, down will come baby, cradle and all.

"I'm innocent!" She pleaded as she knelt before the judge,
"I'm not a bloody murderer! Please don't hold a grudge!"
The jury found her guilty. Not one was moved to tears.
He slammed the gavel on his desk
and gave her 50 years.

I see you're shaking like little leaves, my dear ones. This nursery rhyme will give you nightmares and keep you up all night. Sleep with one eye open, because you never know if Mother will wrap you tightly in a blanket and stuff you in a wooden cradle. Have you been a naughty child? You'll wake up and find yourself on the treetops, bending with the wind in a storm, crashing to the ground.

Mother might get the book thrown at her and end up in jail, but you won't have to worry about that because you'll be dead.

So, my darlings, behave and listen to Mommy Dearest. Remember what happened to that naughty baby.

Rock-A-Bye!

JACK AND JILL

"Jack and Jill went up a hill to fetch a pail of water,
Jack fell down and broke his crown,
Jill came tumbling after".

Another sick nursery rhyme. Scary Fairy will tell you the real meaning of this one.

Never tell angry starving peasants, "Let them eat cake!" You'll be sure to end up at the wrong end of the guillotine and heads will roll. It seems a lot of that went on in those dark bloody days. It was called The French Revolution.

Beheading the royalty was so popular that the peasants made a family day of it. So entertaining! Some even brought picnic baskets and feasted during the executions. Charming French folk.

Let's continue with our nursery rhyme. Queen Marie Antoinette (Jill) bit off more cake than she could chew. King Louis XVI (16th) was our charming Jack. He lost his crown and his head. Marie's head came tumbling after.

I suppose you could say the peasants "Had their cake and ate it too". Revenge is a bitch, isn't it?

Oops! Sorry, my darlings. Enjoy your cake.

THE TALE
OF THE TOOTHLESS
TOOTH FAIRY

Who's the thief who took my teeth?
I didn't put them under my pillow!
I woke up one morning to find them gone,
My smile's like a pad of Brillo!

There's something strange going on at night,
giving children an awful fright!
The Toothless Tooth Fairy is stealing teeth,
to keep them for her own,
Replacing the ones that have fallen out
where her new ones haven't grown.
Her teeth fell out, one by one,
When she smiled, alas, she had none!
She hid her candy under the sheets,
secretly devouring her sugary treats.
Her "sweet tooth" finally took its toll,
as she ate her last tootsie roll.
One after another, her rotten teeth
fell out of her mouth to the ground beneath.
Those shiny new teeth in pink little gums
are tempting to steal in the night.
The Toothless Tooth Fairy will yank them out,
You can't put up a fight!

Children, you're better by far
Ignoring those cookies in the jar!

TOMB OF BONES

There once was a happy family who lived in a very quaint little home on the edge of town. This family consisted of a father, mother, and three small children. One day, the father went into town for some supplies and left his wife alone with the children.

Now, you have to understand that these three youngsters were very mischievous, as children usually are. While their mother was busy doing what mothers do, these little ones found a very big box of matches. A really, really BIG box of matches.

Needless to say, our happy little family was consumed in a huge fire. Flames licked the sky, totally destroying the house and killing all four. When the father returned home, he was devastated, tearing at his hair, screaming in horror to find his home burned to the ground and his entire family killed.

They were buried in a large tomb, a mausoleum of purest marble. Four coffins contained the charred bones of what remained of them. Every day for years, the father visited the tomb, entering with his personal key he had made. He would sit for hours and talk to his dead family in the Tomb of Bones. Opening each casket, he spoke to them as if they were alive. He became obsessed and finally lost his mind.

One night, he dressed himself in a suit, looking quite

dapper. Bringing a bottle of wine and a picnic basket, he unlocked the tomb and began his ritual. Each coffin was opened and they all had a wonderful time together, at least in his mind.

~

He never came out of the Tomb of Bones. When the tomb was opened after years of searching for him, they found a grisly scene.

The father was only a skeleton by now, holding an empty bottle of wine by his side.

Children, please don't play with matches! You could end up in one of those cute little caskets. They come in a variety of colors, too.

HEROIN HIGHWAY

Like the tracks on his arms, the Heroin Highway snaked around the mountains. It was treacherous, slithering menacingly close to the edge of high cliffs. A very deadly fall, indeed!

It was winter. Bitter cold, icy. This road was never meant to be traveled in this weather, but he had to make it to the top to pick up his last batch of heroin. Destination to nowhere. Heroin Highway.

What was he thinking? He was desperate, strung out. He was a junkie. One last fix, one last time and then he'll go to rehab. That's what he kept telling himself for years. It was ice running through his veins. The stuff of nightmares.

Finally reaching the top, he spied a small wooden shack nestled in the ice and snow. Shuffling up the narrow pathway, it reminded him of the broken down shacks he hung out in for days, too high to make it home. Home. Where was that? A small dingy room in a crumbling flop house. That was his life.

Peering out of the icy window was an old man. His black eyes glared wickedly like a spider waiting to eat its prey. Opening the door, he grinned with a toothless smile. "Welcome, my friend. I've been expecting you!"

The addict stared in disbelief at the scarred face. Bony arms riddled with heroin tracks like his, reached out to shake his hand. He recoiled in disgust. The smell of death was all around him.

"Do you think you can leave this earth alive? You're already a dead man!"

The addict knew right then and there what the old man meant. He was already dead. His body was lying on the cockroach infested bed in that flop house. Now he remembered flashing red lights outside the window. The ambulance pulled up and paramedics rushed into his room. He saw himself being given CPR, but to no avail. They took him away in a body bag.

Then he remembered driving on Heroin Highway to get his "last fix". It was all a surreal nightmare. The end of the road for him.

The old man let out a moan and stuck a needle in the addict's arm. "Just one more for the road!"

Remember, children, there is a difference between being a "heroine" and using "heroin". Beware of the Silver Spoon!

SOMETHING SAT ON MY BED LAST NIGHT

(A true scary story from the author)

I was in a dead sleep. Suddenly, I awoke from the pressure on my bed. It felt like someone or something was sitting beside me. I didn't dare turn around. I was frozen. I know "IT" was staring at me.

Then, I felt the pressure lift, as if the presence got up. The feeling was gone. I turned around slowly and to my great relief, saw nothing. I KNOW something came to visit me. What was it?

The next night as I slept, I felt something push me down into the mattress. A very strong pressure was pushing, harder and harder, deeper into my bed, almost to the floor!

I couldn't move, I couldn't scream. It was suffocating me. I thought I was having another nightmare, but I was wide awake!

I saw an evil black shadow on the wall when I opened my eyes. It looked like the devil. Then it disappeared. I know it wasn't a dream. What sat on my bed? What pushed my body through the bed to the floor?

The real question is, what did it want?

LIZZIE

*"Lizzie Borden took an axe
and gave her mother 40 whacks.
When she saw what she had done,
She gave her father 41."*

Poor Lizzie. She got a bad rap.
Who wrote those lyrics?
What a load of crap!

Sorry, kiddies, my language is coarse,
But Scary Fairy has no remorse.
Did Lizzie do it? That's what they say,
Here's what I think,
NO WAY!

There was an uncle on daddy's side,
Who had an "axe to grind".
The brothers didn't get along,
Had words that weren't too kind.

One afternoon while the Bordens slept,
Dear uncle broke in and silently crept.

With axe in hand, he chopped them up when Lizzie wasn't
there,
She returned, oh what a fright,
It was a true nightmare!

No evidence was found against uncle and his murderous
whacks.
That's why poor Lizzie was arrested when they found his
bloody axe.

The jury found her innocent,
No witnesses, no case.
With Lizzie's reputation ruined,
She dared not show her face.

Parents, sleep with one eye open,
Beware how your children play.
Lizzie will never rest in peace,
You might get the axe one day!

SWEET SCREAMS!

When you sleep with covers tight,
I'll whisper in your ear at night.
Wicked tales I spin with glee,
I'm Scary Fairy,
Remember me!

Shadow figures on the wall,
Slimy worms on you will crawl.
Nursery rhymes, don't dare to sing,
Black widow spider's bite will sting.

Goodnight, dear children,
I say adieu,
It was a pleasure scaring you!
Scary Fairy flies away,
Haunting you another day.

WICKEDLY YOURS,

SCARY FAIRY

Scary Fairy has written a short story called "The Ultimate Sacrifice". This is a bonus to her book of wicked fairy tales.

Enjoy the next chapter, but remember one thing...

BE CAREFUL WHAT YOU WISH FOR!!

THE ULTIMATE SACRIFICE

BY SCARY FAIRY

Marni Swanson was a pretty girl, late thirties, blond, blue eyes, about 5'8". She considered herself attractive, yet not a stunner. She attracted men, but relationships never went far. She wasn't interested in a long-term commitment, especially since she was the caregiver for her aging mother.

Ever since her father died in a car accident five years ago, Marni's mom, Camille, sank into a deep depression, an abyss she didn't know how to climb out of. For Marni, this was heartbreaking. She loved her mom, but she hated to see her so ill, digging her own grave. Camille wandered in and out of rooms like a phantom, a thin ghostly woman who was invisible to the world.

Marni's father, Johnny, was found late one summer night drowned in a lake, trapped in his car under an old bridge. With the heavy rain and no lights on the rural roads, he lost control and careened off the bridge, breaking the old railing, crashing head on into the water.

Johnny never made it out. He had been drinking heavily that night. People said they knew it was just a matter of time. That hurt most of all.

In this little Midwestern town, everyone knew everyone's business and gossip ran wild. It was a regular

"Mayberry". Johnny was an alcoholic and didn't seem to take any notice of what other people said about him. It was heartbreaking for Marni and Camille to see his decline over the years. Many nights were marred with hysterical crying and yelling, but thank God there was no physical abuse. Johnny just gave up and passed out most of the time.

Camille was once a beautiful woman, vibrant and full of life. Marni remembered her singing old childhood songs all the time, laughing and tossing her thick strawberry blond hair around her shapely shoulders. At one time, she and Johnny were deeply in love, dancing around the house, eyes for nobody else.

Those were happy years, until Johnny started drinking when he lost his job at the lumber yard. With no more than a high school education, jobs were scarce in this small farm town. Camille's health declined along with her depression. When Johnny was killed in the accident, she just gave up on life. If it wasn't for Marni, there would have been two tombstones in the small cemetery instead of one.

Marni was a nurse in a large hospital a few hours away. That was the only big city nearby. Her commute became too much for her every day, since she had to deal with her mother. Camille didn't want a live-in nurse and became very agitated and angry over the thought of someone else caring for her. The only one she really communicated with was Marni.

So, on that premise, Marni quit the hospital and found a position at a local old age home. The Golden Age Assisted

Living Facility was just ten miles from her home and she welcomed the opportunity to be a valuable contributor in her nursing position.

Lately, she had noticed more of the older residents failing in health, with a few dying this past year. Every time one of them passed away, she thought of her mother. Marni hated to see her deteriorate right before her eyes. Although Camille was in her late seventies, she looked so much older.

One day Marni took a break from the facility and walked to a nearby park. She loved the peacefulness and came here often to gaze on the beautiful lake. Two women were sitting on a long bench, one much older than the other. They were having a very animated conversation. The older woman was upset and crying on the younger one's shoulder. Marni didn't know if she should interrupt, so she approached with caution.

"Excuse me, ladies, would you mind if I sat down with you?" Immediately the two looked at her with curiosity, since she was wearing her uniform from the Home.

"Sure, sit down with us", the older woman quickly answered, wiping away her tears. The younger woman eyed Marni for a few more minutes, then nodded with a strained smile.

"Isn't this a beautiful place?" Marni shifted to the end of

the bench and looked out to the lake. Today was sunny with a light breeze. The ducks were already waddling on the banks quacking loudly.

"Oh yes, we love this place!" Mom and I always feed the ducks when we can. Are you a nurse at the Home over there?"

"Yes, I take care of the residents at "Golden Age". Nice place, close to home. There have been a lot of vacancies lately. Unfortunately, some of them passed away from old age and sickness. No matter how many years I've been nursing, I still can't get used to death. I get attached to them and then grieve like they're my family."

Marni noticed that the two stiffened at this, looking at each other nervously. The mother spoke first.

"I know it's hard to lose someone close to you. We try to support each other the best we can. It's always heartbreaking to see a parent aging or getting sick. That's why mom..er..my daughter, spends so much time with me."

She suddenly grabbed her daughter's hand, knowing she made a critical mistake. Marni sensed a secret between the two women, getting a very strange vibe.

"You live around here, I assume?" Marni quickly answered.

"Yes, yes", the daughter spoke up. There was an awkward silence.

Marni started to explain her history and the fact that she was frightened for her mother's declining health and depression. The two women listened intently, occasionally exchanging knowing glances.

"Well, my dear, maybe you should listen to what we have to tell you. You might think we're crazy, but it's quite a remarkable story. You must know that what we say is the truth, but should go no further."

The mother suddenly turned to her daughter for approval to continue.

"I'm really the daughter. This is my mother!"

The older woman was the daughter? How could this be? The younger woman was really the mother? That seemed ludicrous!

Marni's mouth fell open. She didn't know what to say or how to react. Should she laugh? Maybe not. The two women were very serious. Their eyes were big as saucers, waiting for Marni's reaction.

"But how can this be?" Marni asked, aghast.

"There's a 'wishing cave' nearby, hidden in the thick of the woods. Very few know about it, believe it or not. It has magical powers."

The "mother" continued with her fantastic story.

"There is also a river running through it, sort of a red-tinged pool of water streaming through the cave. Covering the outside of the cave are thick thorns, protecting the entrance. I know this seems like a fairy tale from a Disney movie, but we're telling you the truth from our personal experience."

The "daughter" chimed in. "I can see you're skeptical, like we were at first. I think you're emotionally ready to accept what we're telling you. Mind you, this has consequences beyond our understanding, so don't take this lightly. We don't know how rapidly one will age and the other get younger. The cave decides your fate. Every soul is unique and the cave takes what it wants. You have no control!"

She continued. "Only on a full moon can you hope to get into the cave. I know, a horror story..vampires, werewolves. The thorns part so you can enter. Take two vials of your blood and two vials of your mother's blood. Make your wish and pour the blood into the stream. You will see it turn a deep dark red. If you hope to stop the aging process, you will have to perform the same ritual. Be careful what you wish for, young lady! Sometimes it works, sometimes not. We don't know how fast the aging process will be either. We tried to reverse it, but so far, it's stayed the same. Neither of us has changed in the past few weeks, but God only knows what will happen. It's a curse and we are horribly frightened! It was meant to be for a good purpose, but I think it was a mistake to deal with the devil!"

Marni sat stunned, not sure what to say.

"The moon has magical powers, you're saying? Wow! It's really like a sy-fy movie, but here you are, and if you're telling me the truth, it truly is a miracle!"

The two women didn't crack a smile, stood up and prepared to leave, with a final warning.

"Don't rush into this, dear. It is the ultimate sacrifice! Nobody has yet been able to undo the spell of the wishing cave. The thorns are too thick and it seems that even the full moon is not strong enough at times to get the thorns to part over the entrance."

Marni walked back to the assisted living home, numbed by what she just heard. After she gathered her belongings and checked in on some patients, she headed home.

When she got there, she found her mother on the kitchen floor. Camille had fallen and was unable to get up.

"Mom! What happened? Are you OK? Gee, this is the worst nightmare come true. Come on, stop crying. I'll get you upstairs."

Camille was hysterical, clinging to Marni. Relieved to have her daughter there, she immediately collapsed into bed.

"Mom, go to sleep. I'll tend to you when you wake up. From what I can see, you didn't break any bones and didn't bruise yourself. I'll get you some water and an aspirin. You have to promise to be more careful when you go downstairs, especially."

That was it. That was the deciding moment for Marni. She couldn't bear to see her frail mother deteriorate or lose her memory. If she broke a hip with another fall, that would be the last nail in her coffin.

CHAPTER TWO

The next morning on the premise of getting Camille's blood for an upcoming doctor's visit, Marni took two vials of her own blood and two vials of Camille's. She had a make-shift medical room with equipment she bought from her former employment at the big hospital in the city. Camille didn't question her, but allowed Marni to proceed with the blood samples.

Marni was determined to go through with the wishing cave. She envisioned the mother and daughter again, reversing the aging process. It was an ultimate sacrifice, for sure. She was haunted by the fact that it might not work, that everything was left to chance. This uncertainty sent shivers down her spine, but she made up her mind. It had to happen. She was going to sacrifice part of her youth to give her mother a chance to reverse her aging. She was still young enough to sacrifice a few years!

A disturbing thought lingered. She remembered what they said about the cave's decision to take what it wanted. She had no control over the process. What if it wanted her life in exchange? Marni shook off the thought and went to bed that night tossing and turning in her sleep. Nightmarish visions of her aging into the very old woman she dreaded her mother was going to become flooded her dreams. Who would help her if she was aging too rapidly? Would her mother get her youth back too fast and notice what was happening and panic? She couldn't tell Camille what she was doing or even mention the wishing cave for fear she would think her absolutely crazy. It was all too freaky, too surreal.

The horror show as just beginning. Marni woke up in a sweat, resolute to make her ultimate sacrifice. She had to find the cave.

The next night was perfect. Yes, there was a full moon! Feeling rather ridiculous carrying the vials of blood, Marni made her way to the woods nearby.

She made sure Camille was sound asleep. The sedatives were strong enough to assure Marni she wouldn't wake till morning.

The moon lit up the sky like a glowing orb. She needed it to navigate through the thick trees, even though she brought her own flashlight. All she needed now was a silver bullet or a wooden cross and she'd be the star in a true horror movie. The mother and daughter she met in the park mentioned that the cave would be covered with thick thorns at the entrance. Tramping through the underbrush, it seemed like a lost cause, until finally she saw what looked like a cave.

Through the hazy moonlight streaming through the canopy of trees, she noticed thick thorns surrounding the cave entrance. Touching one thorn carefully, suddenly it moved. Everything moved! The thick mass parted, revealing the cave's narrow entrance, partly covered with moss, like an aging mouth waiting to swallow her whole.

Bending down to squeeze through the narrow entrance, she fumbled in the darkness. Thank God she had her flashlight. It smelled old and damp, like the smell of death she was all too familiar with at the Home. Marni shook off a chill and carefully stepped around a pile of stones as she hugged the cool cave walls. The sound of rushing water just a few feet away gave her an indication that she was near the little stream running through the cave.

There it was! Red, blood red. This was the cave's lifeblood, where she was supposed to sacrifice her youth to save Camille, where she was going to make her ultimate sacrifice. For one moment Marni wanted to bolt out of the cave, run home and forget this ever happened.

Then, she found herself pulling out the vials and chanting words that tumbled uncontrollably out of her mouth. She fervently wished to sacrifice her youth to give years to her mother. She poured the blood into the red stream, now pulsing and wanting more, like an insatiable vampire.

Marni expected something magical to happen, but nothing did. The cave was satisfied with her sacrifice, it seemed. Did it hear her wishes? A sudden moment of clarity came over her. She felt foolish standing there, holding the empty vials, talking to a stream in a dark cave. Thank goodness no one else was there to witness this!

Groping the cave walls, she made it through the entrance. The thorns were closing around the cave. Quickly she pushed through before they completely covered the entrance. What if she was trapped inside and couldn't get out? Shuttering, the full moon was her only companion as she hurried home.

Quietly Marni opened the front door and crept upstairs to her bedroom. She kicked off her boots, then checked on Camille. She was sound asleep. Marni wondered what she would have said if she knew of tonight's escapade.

Days flew by with no change in her or Camille's appearances. Marni was starting to doubt the truth to this fantastic story. Was she taken as a fool by the mother and daughter that day in the park? She felt angry and embarrassed.

After two weeks passed, Marni began to notice a few wrinkles and lines in her face. They weren't there before! She quickly looked at her hands and the rest of her body. She noticed a little sagging and loose skin around her knees. Her butt seemed to drop a bit, too. Of course this upset her, but then she caught herself and laughed at her vanity.

Isn't this what she expected? Half-heartedly, she resigned herself to the awful reality that she will start to age, and her mother will look younger. Mom! She rushed to the bedroom where Camille was supposed to be asleep at this hour. Nowhere! Where was she? Panicking, Marni pictured her mother lying on the floor, falling down the stairs or something worse.

Quickly running downstairs, Marni suddenly stopped cold. Camille was singing in the kitchen making breakfast!

"Wow, mom!" Marni exclaimed in awe. "I didn't think you'd be up this early."

Camille turned around, her face glowing. The lines around her eyes and mouth were completely gone. She really looked younger. Marni kissed her on the cheek and said, "You look like you've lost a few years! Where did you get all this energy?"

Camille gave her a strange look and tilted her head to study Marni's face.

"And you look like you could use a few more hours of sleep! Why do you look so tired? Come on, have some breakfast, Marni. And, yes, I feel terrific for a change. I don't know what it is, but I got out of bed without help, put on my clothes, looked in the mirror and couldn't believe how refreshed I look!"

Bittersweet moment, awkward silence.

"Mom, I think it's the meds you've been taking. I'm so happy to see you smiling again."

After breakfast Marni headed out for the Home. She didn't look forward to facing all the sick and lonely ones. Hopefully this aging process would slow down and stop before she became "one of them". God forbid! A cold bony finger slithered down her spine, chilling her to the very marrow. She shivered, and a cold sweat bathed her face. Little did she know her nightmare was just beginning.

CHAPTER THREE

Every morning Marni feared seeing herself in the mirror. What would she see this time? Whose face would be staring back at her? She could feel her body declining in strength. She certainly could see her skin thinning. Blue veins in her hands popped out like thin little rivers running through them. Small clumps of those blue veins covered her legs and feet.

On the other side of the house she heard a shriek coming from Camille's bedroom. Marni rushed to her mother. Camille was standing naked in front of the long mirror, staring in disbelief. Her body was supple and lean, almost wrinkle-free. Marni let out a gasp. When Camille saw Marni looking at her from the doorway, she became aware of her nakedness and reached for her nightgown.

"My God, Marni! It's a miracle! Look at me! Look at me! What's happening?"

Radiant, she smiled, but quickly stopped when she studied Marni's face. She saw an aging old woman staring at her with her mouth open. Terrified, Camille stepped back, sitting on the bed.

"Mom, what is it?" Marni panicked, her heart racing. Camille looked as if she saw a ghost.

"Marni, what's happening to you and me? Every

morning I look in the mirror and it seems I'm getting younger and younger. It's a miracle I think!"

∾

Marni felt very old and tired all of a sudden. She struggled to tell her of the blood, the wishing cave, the deal with the devil. No words came out of her quivering mouth. She swallowed, trying to smile.

"Mom, I don't know what miracle this is, but I'm so happy that you're feeling healthy again and looking so young!"

Camille had a frightened look, horrified to see her daughter's face, sagging with wrinkles like an old woman.

"Honey, you're looking very sickly. Are you getting any sleep? I've noticed how you seem to be aging overnight, while I'm getting younger. Is this possible? Am I dreaming or in some kind of sick "Twilight Zone" episode? It doesn't feel right."

Marni hugged her mother, quietly rocking her. She tried to hide her tears, but they just kept falling. Camille turned to look at her, seeing only a shell of her daughter. She was gradually disappearing in front of her eyes.

It was a balmy night, one of those sticky heavy evenings when nothing moved. Even the crickets were silent. Marni sat on the porch, hunched over her tea, deep in thought. It seemed she was always pensive lately, always frightened.

Her body was sagging and her bones hurt, just like the heavy weight of the evening. Camille appeared in the doorway. She saw Marni and slipped behind her, hugging her frail shoulders.

"Hey, baby girl! What a quiet night it is. My God, it's hot." She wiped her forehead and sat down next to Marni.

Marni slowly turned her face toward Camille and nodded. Camille smelled like sweet jasmine perfume, the smell of youth. All of her energy was sapped from her mind and body. She couldn't bring herself to say anything, almost as if her tongue was glued to the top of her mouth.

Camille stared at her with a fearful look, but quickly faked a smile.

"Honey, I've been meaning to ask you something. Are you hiding anything from me? I've noticed you've been looking old and haggard these past few weeks and I want to help you if you're sick. Are you sick? Is it cancer, for Christ's sake?"

Her voice cracked as it hit a high note. Marni noticed tears welling up in her eyes. She held out her wrinkled hand and grabbed Camille's arm.

"Mom, I'm going to see a doctor tomorrow, I promise. I don't want to alarm you, so let's not panic, OK? It's not cancer, don't worry. Now, please leave me alone and I'll see you in the morning. It's going to be a full moon all week and I just want to stay out here a while longer. It seems to have a calming effect on me."

Camille sighed and kissed Marni on her graying head. A full moon! Marni caught her breath. She had to reverse the spell somehow. What did they tell her about stopping the curse? She tried to piece together their conversation in the park that day, but she was gradually losing her memory.

Oh, yes! Two more vials of blood each..full moon.. open thorns to get to the cave..the red stream of blood..try to reverse the spell.

Oh, and another thing. It might not work.

Marni was resolute now. She slowly got up and went into the house, determined to end this. She was dying of old age, while her mother was getting younger every day. She had to get to the cave tomorrow night. It was going to be another full moon.

The next morning Marni was on a mission. Camille protested taking another two vials of blood from her.

"Why do you need so much blood from me, Marni? I don't have a doctor's appointment and I'm feeling fine. You're the one who needs help, darling!"

Marni ignored her pleas and proceeded to take her blood, then took two vials of her own blood. Camille continued to whimper and left the room. As she was leaving, she turned to Marni in a loud voice.

"Marni, I just don't understand you anymore! You quit your job, you look awful, and you won't tell me anything. What's wrong with you? I'm going into town for a few hours. Please talk to me when I get back. I love you, baby!"

Marni didn't answer. She was too exhausted to fight, even too tired to say 'I love you too, mom!' The last two vials of blood sapped all her energy. She curled up on the couch and closed her weary eyes.

She thought to herself, 'Tonight. It has to be tonight or I'll die of old age, and that's the end of my life, the absolute end!'

She cried herself to sleep.

CHAPTER FOUR

Camille returned from shopping in town. She bought new clothes to fit her new body, proud of the fact she had a youthful wardrobe. When she opened the front door, she noticed Marni sleeping on the couch and covered her with a blanket, then went upstairs to bed.

When Marni awoke, she parted the curtains and saw the full moon shining big and bright, hypnotizing her as if in a trance. With determination, she gathered the vials of blood and her flashlight. Wearily she slipped into her running shoes. Ah, those sneakers she loved so much when she could run for miles! Ironic, wasn't it? A slight smile crossed her thin face, a bitter smile from a bitter old woman.

It was all her fault. She had nobody to blame but herself. Out of love of her mother, she had made an unselfish sacrifice. The ultimate sacrifice! Now it was time to put an end to this curse, if she could. She didn't want to dance with the devil anymore.

Marni checked on Camille before she left the house. It was so hard to climb those infernal stairs. Her knees hurt as she slowly shuffled to the bedroom. Camille was asleep, looking like an angel. She was so young and happy, even smiling in her sleep. Marni felt a twinge of remorse in the pit of her stomach. There was a jealous moment when she envied her mother, but that quickly passed. What a shame it would be to reverse the aging process and see Camille aging again like the old woman Marni had become.

She shook it off. Now was not the time for regrets. Now was the time for action.

The moon was so bright it served as a beaming guide, illuminating the woods. Marni carefully maneuvered her way through the dense foliage, almost tripping on scattered logs and thick underbrush. This was a totally different trip from the last one. The first time she did this she was a lot younger.

Breathing heavily, she stopped to catch her breath. Now it was almost impossible to see where she was going, even with the moonlight and her flashlight. She held tightly to the bag containing the vials of blood.

Suddenly she felt a sharp pain in her chest. Was she having a heart attack? Clutching her chest she pushed forward, hoping she would recognize the thick thorns guarding the cave. Where was it? Gasping in labored breaths, Marni saw in the distance what she thought was the cave. So close, yet so far!

"My God! Please let it be the cave! Please don't let me die here!"

Just as she reached the circle of thorns, Marni groaned and fell backwards, tossing the bag in the air. She hit her head on the rocks. Eyes open to the night sky, she took her last breath and died along the dirt path. That instant, the wall of thorns opened up, dripping blood around the cave's entrance. It had taken what it wanted. It had taken Marni's life.

The mocking moon was no friend that night. It glared wickedly at the old woman lying on the ground.

Marni died making her ultimate sacrifice, her very soul.

CHAPTER FIVE

Sunshine streamed through the bedroom window, as a new day arrived. Camille felt the sun on her face. She rolled over in bed and yawned, peaceful and happy.

Her feet touched the floor with a bounce, as she rushed to the long mirror. She couldn't believe how beautiful and young she looked! Face flushed with excitement, she danced naked around the room, admiring her new body. Today was a special day, a magical day!

She would get dressed and make breakfast for her and Marni. She had so much to share with Marni now that she could remember everything like it was yesterday.

'Yes!' She thought to herself. 'It's going to be a perfect day, just Marni and me!'

Twirling and dancing around the room, Camille was laughing just like a child.

THE WICKED END

THE REAL SCARY FAIRY

DONNA